contents

yay! Let's play!

LittleBrother BOOKS

Published 2020.

Little Brother Books Ltd, Ground Floor, 23 Southernhay East, Exeter, Devon EX1 1QL

books@littlebrotherbooks.co.uk | www.littlebrotherbooks.co.uk

Printed in Poland.

The Little Brother Books trademark, email and website addresses, are the sole and exclusive properties of Little Brother Books Limited.

moose™

Under License By:
© MOOSE ENTERPRISE PTY LTD, 2020
29 GRANGE ROAD, CHELTENHAM
VIC 3192, AUSTRALIA
www.moosetoys.com
info@moosetoys.com

yay, Let's Play!

Hello, and welcome to Rainbow Kindi!

Ms R Bow is waiting to meet you, and so are your new friends! We're going to have so much fun playing together. Let's start our adventure.

WHAT'S YOUR NAME?

write it here so your new friends can say hello.

HELLO!
MY NAME IS

I'M A KINDI KID

Knock on the door and let's go inside!

KNOCK, KNOCK!

it's cool to be kindi!

welcome to rainbow kindi!

Marsha Mello

A little softie that's as sweet as candy!

Donatina

Full of fun and worry-free.

Peppa-Mint

Shy and super-sweet.

Mystabella

Mystabella is destined for the stage and loves putting on a show!

Cindy Pops

Cindy Pops loves playing Doctors!

Beary Chill

Open up the fridge for some food play fun!

Ms R Bow

She's such fun, and always there to help.

it's time to meet your new friends!

Rainbow Kate

Bright and colourful.

Jessicake

Loves baking and making friends!

Summer Peaches

An imagination for storytelling like no other!

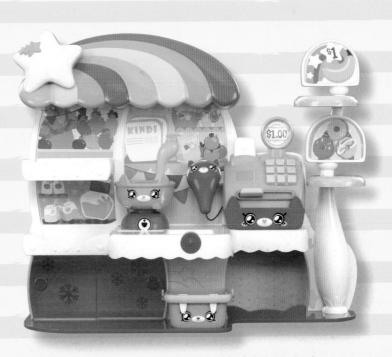

Friendship Chair

Curl up here for some cute quiet time.

Kitty Supermarket

You can pick up all your Kindi shopping here. Pop it into Bunny Cart, and pay at the Kitty Cash register!

SPOT THE DIFFERENCE

Jessicake is holding a cupcake party for Marsha Mello and Peppa-Mint.

1

Colour a cupcake each time you spot a difference.

sweetness overload!

2

Draw a circle around the Jessicake that is the odd one out.

a

b

c

d

Answers on pages 76-77.

CHILL OUT

Help Rainbow Kate sort
Beary Chill's sweet snacks.

Count the snacks. How many are there?

4   2   3   1

BACKPACK, BAGS PACKED!

it's cool to be kindi!

The Kindi Kids are almost ready to go!

Follow the lines to see which girl gets which backpack.

Answers on pages 76-77.

13

LiL' SOFTiE!

Marsha loves anything cute, cuddly and colourful!

1 Draw three more marshmallows for Marsha.

2 Tick the frame that has more stars in it.

a   Bobble 'n' bounce!   **b**

 Use this number line to help you count.

| 1 | 2 | 3 | 4 | 5 | 6 | 7 | 8 | 9 | 10 |

Answers on pages 76-77.

Bring Marsha Mello to life with lots of cute colour!

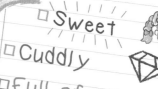

Marsha Mello is...

☐ Sweet

☐ Cuddly

☐ Full of energy!

SO PUZZLING

Jessicake has found a puzzle in the Kindi cupboard!

Draw lines to help Jessicake put the jigsaw pieces back into the right spot.

BFFs are the best!

a

b

c

d

SWEET FRIENDS!

These Kindi Kids are all the same… or are they?

Circle the odd girl out in each row!

1
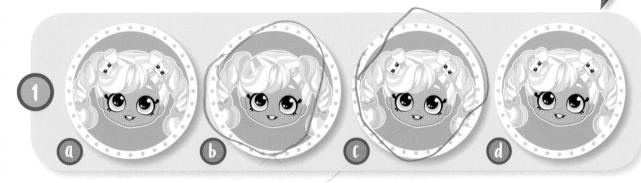
a b c d

2

a b c d

3

a b c d

4

a b c d

Answers on pages 76-77.

Kindi friends for life!

GET UP AND GO!

It's time for a fun game with Ms R Bow.

You'll need

- Scissors
- Sticky tape

Instructions

- Carefully cut around the outline of the dice on the facing page.

- Fold along the lines to make a dice shape, and secure with sticky tape.

Jessicake says play pretend teachers!

Peppa-Mint says point to someone kind.

How to play

- This is a game for up to four players.

- Players take it in turns to throw the dice.

- Each player carries out the task on the dice.

read PAGE 20 before cutting out the dice or scan this page and print it out.

Ask a grown-up for help with scissors.

Bounce around like Marsha Mello

Donatina says do five star jumps!

Jessicake says play pretend teachers!

Peppa-Mint says point to someone kind.

Summer Peaches says sing a silly song!

Shout out three colours for Rainbow Kate

out three colours Rainbow Kate

Summer Peaches says sing a silly song!

Sweet friends!

LET'S BAKE!

Jessicake always has something tasty cooking!

Colour in an apron for Jessicake.
Give each cupcake a different topping.

Flower

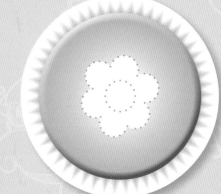

Cute panda

Sun

you bake my day!

20

Jessicake is...

☐ Sweet

☐ Smart

☐ Always trying new things

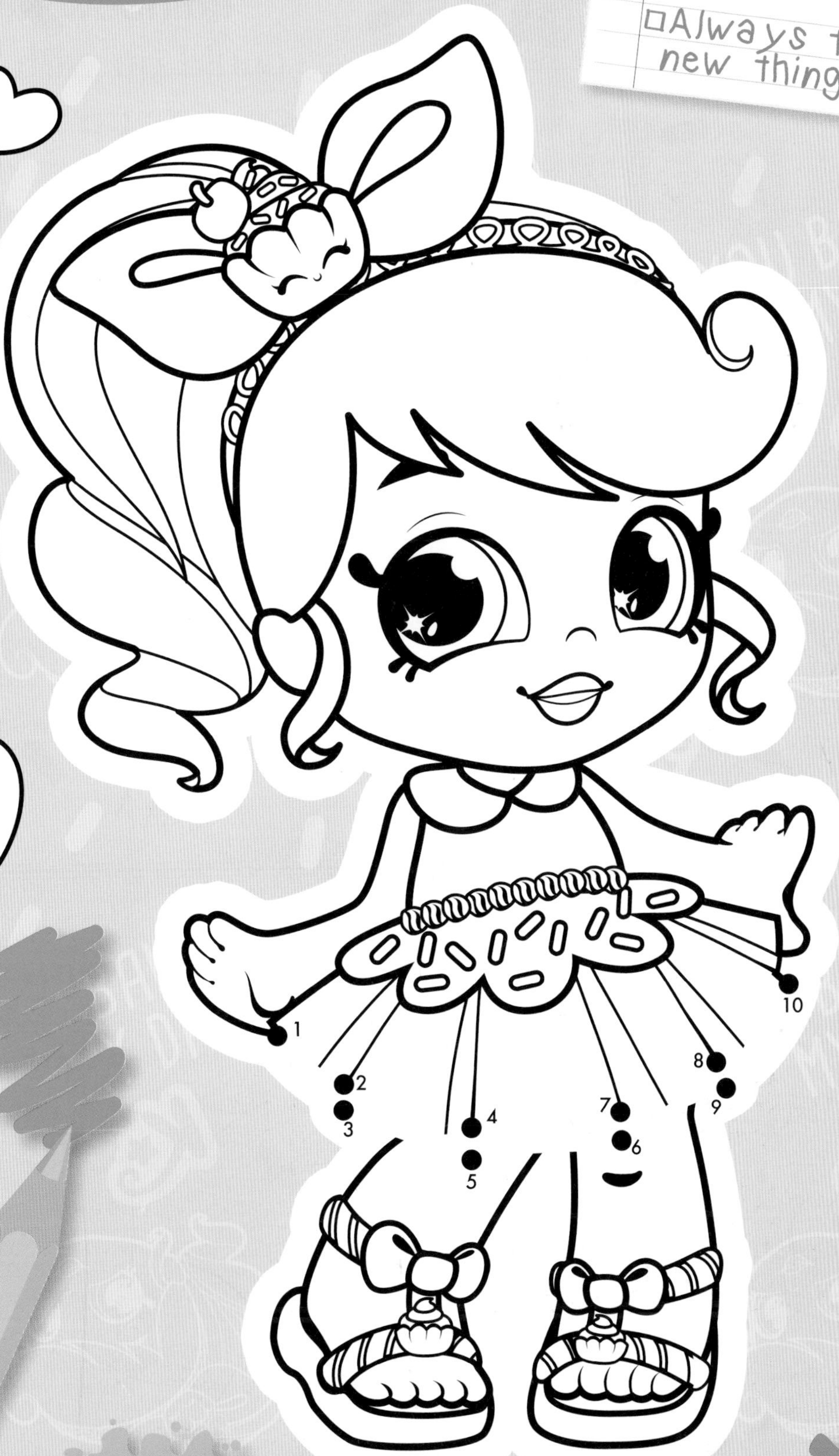

1
2
3
4
5
6
7
8
9
10

Colour in the picture.

21

PUT AWAY THE TOYS

Rainbow Kindi could do with some tidy up time!

Can you find

1.
2.
3.

MAKE A RAINBOW

Rainbow Kate is bursting with cool colour!

Finish the rainbow for Rainbow Kate.
Trace around the clouds.

Chase the rainbow!

What's your favourite colour?

colour it here!

24

LET'S COUNT!

It's easy as 1, 2, 3!

1   1 + 1 =

BFF

2   Draw one more star.

3   Count all the Kindi Kids

peppa-mint   jessicake   marsha mello   donatina

1   2   3   4

FRIENDS FOREVER

Follow Marsha Mello and Rainbow Kate's tips to be Kindi friends for life!

Tick each one!

1. Give your friends a hug.

2. Be kind to everyone.

3. Share your toys.

4. Always be nice.

5. Play with your friends.

Wow, what a sweet friend you are, just like Marsha Mello.

MY KINDNESS TO DO LIST

WRITE YOUR NAME HERE:

How to use your list.

1. Pick a kind challenge every day.
2. Tick it off when you've completed it.

☐ TODAY I'LL BE KIND TO SOMEONE.

☐ TODAY I'LL HELP PUT THE TOYS AWAY.

☐ TODAY I WILL SAY PLEASE AND THANK YOU.

☐ TODAY I'LL SHARE MY TOYS.

☐ TODAY I'LL BE A GOOD LISTENER.

☐ TODAY I'LL BE NICE TO EVERYBODY.

☐ TODAY I'LL GIVE SOMEONE A HUG.

☐ TODAY I'LL HELP WITHOUT BEING ASKED.

☐ TODAY I'LL MAKE MY BED.

Kindness Challenge

29

¡I DREAM OF ICE CREAM!

Peppa-Mint loves ice-cream sandwiches.
Create some yummy treats for her.

Trace over the dots.

doodle some SPRINKLES.

draw your own ice-cream here.

SHINE BRIGHT!

Draw lines to join the clouds in the correct
order from 1-10 to reach the rainbow.

1

2

3

Use this
number line
to help you
count.

32

1 2 3 4 5

PLAY TIME

The friends are having so much fun at Rainbow Kindi.

1

Colour a heart each time you spot a difference.

Can you spot six differences between the two pictures?

2

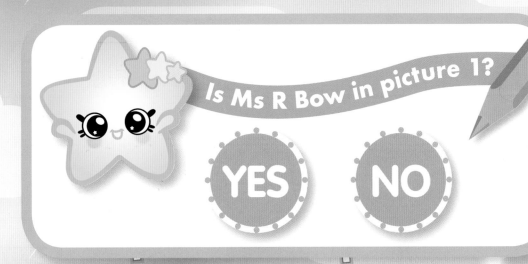

Is Ms R Bow in picture 1?

YES   NO

SNACK ATTACK!

The friends are hungry. Help them find the right snacks.

1

Rainbow Kate wants a banana.

◯

◯

2

Donatina wants a pink soda.

◯

◯

3

Marsha Mello wants cereal.

◯

◯

4

Peppa-Mint wants a strawberry.

◯

◯

LET'S BOUNCE!

SOOO MELLO!

Follow Marsha Mello as she jumps around the kindi!

1 Zig zag

Up... down... Up... down... Up... down...

2 Bouncy

Boing!

3 Round and round

Wheee!

37

KINDI FRIENDS UNITE

Race the girls through the maze to reach the backpack

Grab your friends and see who reaches the bag first.

START

START

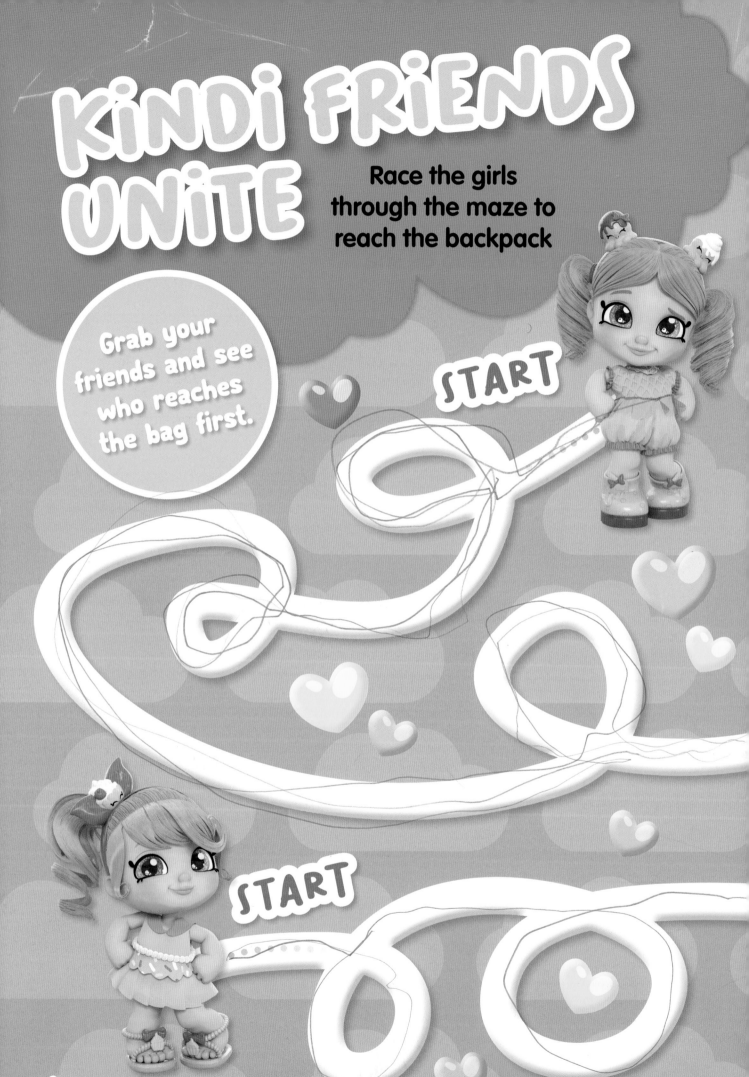

38

START

START

39

SUPERMARKET DASH

Follow the trail to the tills, following the instructions as you go.

START

draw around the bunny cart so you can start shopping

HOW MANY CANS ARE THERE?

2   3

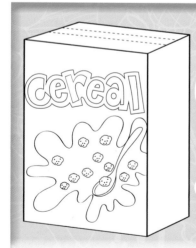

COLOUR in the CEREAL PACK.

FINISH

Well done, you've got all the shopping. Pretend to pay.

BOBBLE YOUR HEAD!

Try following some of the moves from the Bobble Song.

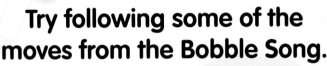

CAN YOU BOBBLE YOUR HEAD?

CAN YOU BOBBLE YOUR ARMS?

CAN YOU BOBBLE YOUR NOSE?

CAN YOU BOBBLE YOUR LEGS?

CAN YOU BOBBLE YOUR BELLY?

BOBBLE BOBBLE BOBBLE

JUST LIKE YOU'RE JELLY.

41

WHAT COMES NEXT?

Draw lines to put the correct character into the pattern.

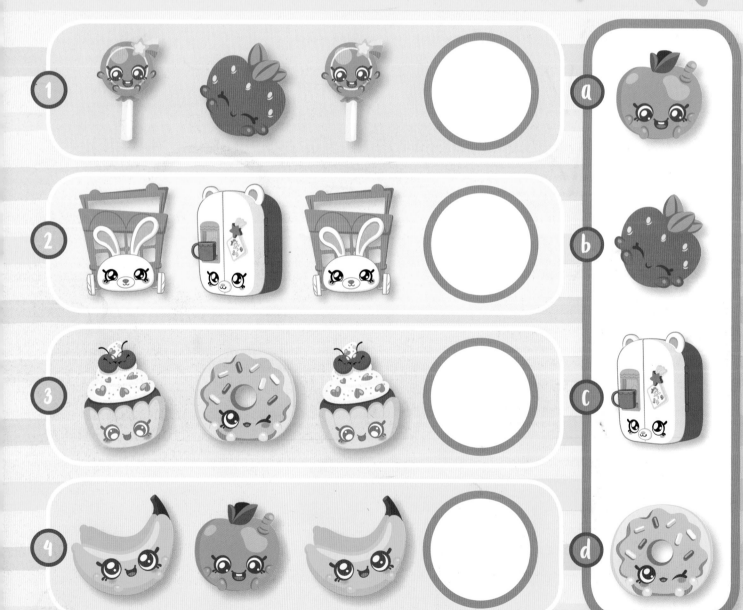

Answers on pages 76-77.

LET'S PLAY SHOPS

Join Rainbow Kate on some shopping fun.

read page 44 before cutting out the coins or scan this page and print it out.

Cut out the coins.

Ask a grown-up for help with scissors.

Draw a pattern on the purse. Now pretend to put your coins in it.

Colour in the cash register.

Write your name on the debit card.

BANK

1234 5678 9000 0000

43

MAKE NEW FRIENDS

Get ready to play all day with these friendship tips.

Friendship Chair's tips

SMILE

SAY HELLO!

ASK THEM WHAT THEIR NAME IS.

Summer Peaches' tips

AND DON'T FORGET TO TELL THEM YOURS.

ASK IF THEY WANT TO PLAY.

MAKE THEM FEEL WELCOME.

HiDE AND SEEK!

Find all the Kindi Kids friends hiding in the picture below.

CAN YOU FIND:

GET READY FOR KINDI

48

Tick the list to get ready for Rainbow Kindi with Rainbow Kate.

Tick each one!

1. Make your bed. ✓
2. Wash your face. ✓
3. Clean your teeth. ✓
4. Get dressed. ✓
5. Eat breakfast.

clean your teet

Well done! You're ready to go.

GET DOODLING

Decorate a backpack for Kindi,
just like Rainbow Kate's.

add your name to
the tag and make it
totally your style!

NAME:
Juliet

DONUT WORRY... BE HAPPY!

Donatina is one cute Kindi Kid!

Donatina is...

- ☐ Sassy
- ☐ Enthusiastic
- ☐ Lots of fun!

Decorate Donatina's bow so she's Kindi-ready for a fun-packed day!

51

BORN TO SiNG

Time to take the spotlight!

1 Count all the musical notes on the page.

How many did you count?

2 Which microphone matches Mystabella's?

a

b

c

Answers on pages 76-77.

Mystabella is all about the candy coloured stripes! See if you can copy them into this picture.

Mystabella is...

☐ Creative
☐ Sweet
☐ A born performer

53

CLOTHES CLOSE UP

Can you tell which bow belongs to which Kindi Kid?

Draw lines to match the beautiful bows and shoes to the correct Kindi kid.

a

b

c

Donatina   **Jessicake**   **Marsha Mello**

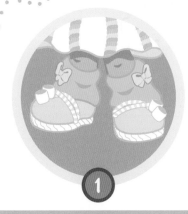
1

2

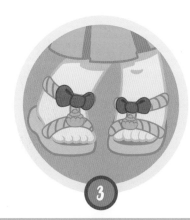
3

Answers on pages 76-77.

STORE CUPBOARD STOCK TAKE

Help Summer Peaches count all the items

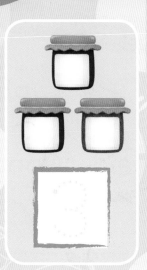

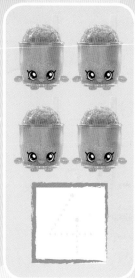

1. How many coins?

2. How many cookie boxes?

3. How many jam jars?

4. How many slushies?

5. How many tins?

Now shout out all the numbers, counting backwards from five. Get to one, and shout, 'Kindi Kids!'

55

STARRING... YOU!

Fill in your name and be the little star of the story!

Write your name wherever you see the gap, then read out the story with a grown-up.

One day _____ joined the Kindi.

Ms R Bow said "Good morning,

class, this is _____". All the

Kindi Kids came to say hello to

_____ and soon _____

had made lots of new friends.

"Thanks for making me feel welcome,"

said _____. "Here's to lots

more adventures tomorrow!"

EYE SPY

See how many of these things you and your grown-up can spot next time you're out and about.

Tick the ones you spot!

1 Leaf

2 Tree

3 Worm

4 Flower

5 Squirrel

6 Bird

Did you spot everything?
Well done, draw yourself a big star!

57

DOODLE 'N' DRAW

Follow the coloured dots, then finish off this scene with some bright colours!

Match your crayons to the numbers!

1

2

3

Match your crayons to the numbers!

1
2
3

Match your crayons to the numbers!

1
2
3

READY FOR CLASS

Follow the trails to see who is first to greet Ms R Bow this morning!

Rainbow Kate

Marsha Mello

Summer Peaches

Answers on pages 76-77.

STOP, LOOK, THINK!

Can you spot who is missing from the pictures? Tick the ones missing!

WHO IS IT?

- [ ] Peppa-Mint
- [ ] Donatina
- [ ] Jessicake

WHO IS IT?

- [ ] Ms R Bow
- [ ] Lettuce
- [ ] Cupcake